Maths

The 11+
10-Minute Tests

For the CEM (Durham University) test

Ages
10-11

Practise • Prepare • Pass

Everything your child needs for 11+ success

How to use this book

This book is made up of 10-minute tests and puzzle pages.
There are answers and detailed explanations in the pull-out section at the back of the book.

10-Minute Tests

- There are 31 tests in this book, each containing 12 questions.

- Each test is designed to cover a good range of the question styles and topics that your child could come across in the maths section of their 11+ test, at the same difficulty level.

- Your child should aim to score around 10 or 11 out of 12 in each 10-minute test. If they score less than this, use their results to work out the areas they need more practice on.

- If your child hasn't managed to finish the test in time, they need to work on increasing their speed, whereas if they have made a lot of mistakes, they need to work more carefully.

- Keep track of your child's scores using the progress chart on the inside back cover of the book.

Puzzle Pages

- There are 6 puzzle pages in this book, which are a great break from test-style questions. They encourage children to practise the same skills that they will need in the test, but in a fun way.

Published by CGP

Editors:
Paul Jordin, Ben Train, Jonathan Wray

With thanks to Sharon Keeley-Holden and Maxine Petrie for the proofreading.

Please note that CGP is not associated with CEM or The University of Durham in any way.
This book does not include any official questions and it is not endorsed by CEM or The University of Durham.
CEM, *Centre for Evaluation and Monitoring, Durham University* and *The University of Durham*
are all trademarks of The University of Durham.

ISBN: 978 1 78294 259 7
Printed by Elanders Ltd, Newcastle upon Tyne
Clipart from Corel®

Based on the classic CGP style created by Richard Parsons.

Contents

You have **10 minutes** to do this test. Work as quickly and accurately as you can.

Sean checks his gas meter reading. The meter reading is shown below.

T H T U
| 2 | 7 | 8 | 6 | 6 | 1 |

1. What is the reading on the meter rounded to the nearest thousand?

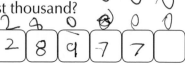

| 2 | 8 | 9 | 7 | 7 | |

2. He checks the reading again six months later. It has increased by 842.
   What is the new meter reading?

| 2 | 8 | 9 | 5 | 0 | 3 |

Lisa is reading a book. The number of pages she reads
each day in one week is shown in a bar chart.

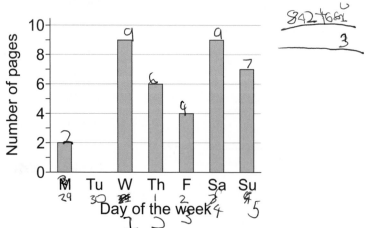

3. How many pages of the book does Lisa read at the weekend?

| 1 | 6 |

4. The date on the Monday is 29th April.
   How many pages does Lisa read on 3rd May?

| 0 | 9 |

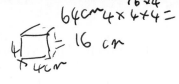

5. What is the volume of a cube with sides of length 5 cm?
Circle the correct option.

16 × 4

A   25 cm³
B   125 cm³ ✓
C   100 cm³
D   15 cm³
E   50 cm³

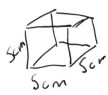

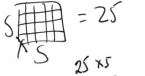

Kevin buys a box of corn flakes for £1.40 and some chocolate for £1.50.
Using these ingredients, he makes corn flake cakes, and sells them for £1 each.

6. What's the smallest number of cakes Kevin has to sell in order to make a profit?

0 3

7. If Kevin sells ten corn flake cakes, how much profit does he make?

£ 0 7 . 1 0

8. Each cake is made with 20 g of corn flakes and 15 g of chocolate.
What is the total mass of 60 corn flake cakes? Circle the correct option.

A   28 000 g
B   2.1 kg
C   1.8 kg
D   2400 g
E   240 g

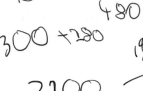

9. What is the sum of the only two prime numbers between 50 and 60?

10. Which of the following statements is true? Circle the correct option.

    A $16 \times 30 > 8 \times 60$ ✗

    B $15 \times 30 < 30 \times 15$ ✗

    C $20 \times 25 = 10 \times 12.5$ ✗

    D $8 \times 24 = 9 \times 48$ ✓

    E $45 \times 1000 > 900 \times 100$

less than   *greater than?*

$$\begin{array}{r} 85 \times \\ 4 \\ \hline 320 \; + 20 + 1 \\ \hline 341 \end{array}$$

11. A sequence starts 1, 5, 21, 85, ...
Each term is found by multiplying the previous term by 4 and adding on 1.

Which of these numbers does not appear in the sequence?
Circle the correct option.

    A   341

    B   1365

    C   5461

    D   21 845

    E   87 318

12. Jane uses the formula $E = 8x + 3$ to work out how much money she earns in a day, where E is her earnings in pounds and x is the number of hours worked.
One day she earned £91.

How many hours did she work that day?

                  hours

/ 12

You have **10 minutes** to do this test. Work as quickly and accurately as you can.

1. On the coordinate grid, point P is moved 7 squares right and 2 squares down.

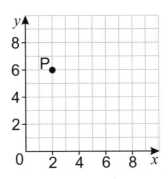

What are the new coordinates of point P?

2. In which of the following numbers does the 6 have the smallest value?
    Circle the correct option.

    A   160523

    B   22864

    C   797617.5

    D   8926.53

    E   60.0849

3. One of the angles in a right-angled triangle is 72°.

    Which of the following is also an angle in the triangle? Circle the correct option.

    A   18°

    B   108°

    C   96°

    D   26°

    E   38°

Sundeep has eight pencils on his desk. The lengths of the pencils are listed below.

7 cm, 12 cm, 14 cm, 9 cm, 16 cm, 6 cm, 7 cm, 3 cm

4. Sundeep arranges the pencils in order of increasing length, starting with the shortest on the left. What is the length of the pencil which is fourth from the right?

 cm

5. He then picks up the three longest pencils. What is the mean length of these three pencils?

cm

6. Dr. Kapur has a 5 litre jug of water. She pours half on her plants, then gives 1600 ml to patients. How much water is left? Circle the correct option.

A 900 ml		**C** 0.8 l		**E** 1100 ml
B 1.3 l		**D** 2400 ml		

Julie is watching a film. After 35 minutes, she has watched 25% of the film.

7. What is the total length of the film? Circle the correct option.

A 2 hours 10 minutes
B 3 hours 10 minutes
C 2 hours 45 minutes
D 1 hour 40 minutes
E 2 hours 20 minutes

8. Julie starts watching the film at 13:45.
She pauses the film for 5 minutes halfway through, to make a cup of tea.
What time does she finish watching the film?
Give your answer in 24-hour clock format.

☐☐:☐☐

9. Tony's lasagne recipe is for 12 people, and needs 800 ml of tomato sauce.
   If Tony makes a lasagne for 18 people, how much tomato sauce does he need?

 ml

10. James wants to run at least 500 m by doing laps
    around the perimeter of a park, shown below.

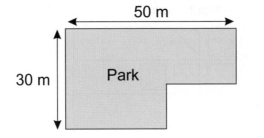

50 m

30 m   Park

not to scale

What is the smallest number of whole laps that he must run?

11. If $4(x + 5) = 44$, what is x? Circle the correct option.

    A   8   **C**   6   **E**   7
    B   11   **D**   35

12. A triangle has sides with lengths a, b and c.

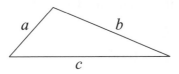

a b

c

Which of the following statements is definitely not true? Circle the correct option.

    A $a + b > c$
    B $c + b = 18$
    C $b > a + c$
    D $0 < b + a$
    E $a < b < c$

/ 12

You have **10 minutes** to do this test. Work as quickly and accurately as you can.

Gerard sells four types of sandwich in his cafe.
He records the number of each type of sandwich sold on one day in a pictogram.

Sandwich	Amount sold
Piccalilli	⬜⬜⬜◥
Ham and cheese	⬜⬜⬜⬜⬜
BLT	⬜▷
Egg mayo	⬜⬜⬜▷

⬜ = 4 sandwiches

1.   How many more piccalilli sandwiches were sold than BLT on that day?

2.   Gerard's profit from selling each ham and cheese sandwich is £1.50.
      How much does he make from selling ham and cheese sandwiches that day?

      £ ⬜⬜.⬜⬜

3.   Which of the following is the smallest? Circle the correct option.

      A   4%   **C** $^3/_{100}$ **E** $^1/_{20}$
      B   0.65   **D**   0.065

4.   An empty steel bucket has a mass of 850 g. When it is filled with sand,
      it has a mass of 16.2 kg. What is the total mass of the sand in the bucket?
      Circle the correct option.

      A   15 550 g   **C**   17 050 g   **E**   14 650 g
      B   15 350 g   **D**   16 950 g

5. Tifah makes a cube with sides of length 2 cm out of card. What is the area of the net that she needs to make the cube? Circle the correct option.

    A   8 cm²

    B   16 cm²

    C   20 cm²

    D   24 cm²

    E   32 cm²

6. Chris leaves his house, and is out for four hours and twenty minutes, before arriving back at his house at 7:15 pm. At what time did he leave his house?

$$\boxed{}\,\boxed{} : \boxed{}\,\boxed{} \text{ pm}$$

7. Jonah has a bag with red balls and blue balls. The bag contains twice as many red balls as blue balls. What fraction of balls in the bag are blue? Circle the correct option.

    A $^1/_3$ **C** $^2/_3$ **E** $^3/_7$

    B $^1/_2$ **D** $^2/_5$

8.

x

216°

49°   31°

not drawn accurately

What is the size of angle x?

$$\boxed{}\,\boxed{}\,\boxed{}\,^\circ$$

9. What is $49 \times 138 - 37 \times 49$?

$$\boxed{}\,\boxed{}\,\boxed{}\,\boxed{}$$

A sequence is made by joining together squares with sides of length 1.

Shape 1	Shape 2	Shape 3	Shape 4
Perimeter = 4	Perimeter = 6	Perimeter = 8	Perimeter = 10

10. Which expression gives the perimeter of the *n*th shape? Circle the correct option.

    A   4*n*   **C**   3*n* + 4   **E**   2*n* + 2

    B   4*n* − 1   **D**   3*n* + 1

11. What is the perimeter of Shape 94?

12.

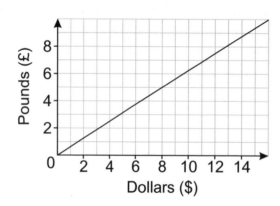

Dollars ($)

Rachel has £8. Simon has $12. Who has more money, and by how much?
Use the conversion graph to give an estimate. Circle the correct option.

    A   Rachel has about $0.40 more than Simon.

    B   Rachel has about $0.80 more than Simon.

    C   Rachel has about £1.50 more than Simon.

    D   Simon has about $2.50 more than Rachel.

    E   Simon has about £0.20 more than Rachel.

/ 12

You have **10 minutes** to do this test. Work as quickly and accurately as you can.

1. The peak temperature in Vanville one year was 18 °C. The lowest temperature in the same year was –25 °C. What was the difference between the highest and lowest temperatures in Vanville that year?

    ⬚⬚ °C

2. Which number is a factor of both 48 and 27? Circle the correct option.

    A 2
    B 3
    C 4
    D 7
    E 9

3. The heights of Janet's plants are 19 cm, 25 cm, 28 cm and 32 cm.
    What is the mean height of Janet's plants?

    ⬚⬚ cm

4. The sizes of three of the angles in a quadrilateral are 47°, 133° and 95°.
    What is the size of the missing angle? Circle the correct option.

    A 108°
    B 85°
    C 25°
    D 125°
    E 90°

5. Work out the area of the shape below.

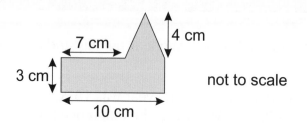

not to scale

[ ][ ][ ] cm²

6. A company has crates that weigh 14.68 kg each. A shipping container can hold 1024 crates. What is the total weight of the crates in one full container? Circle the correct option.

   A   35 191.2 kg

   B   15 032.32 kg

   C   52 510.8 kg

   D   117 493.2 kg

   E   205 265.4 kg

The prices of some of the items sold in a DIY shop are shown below.

7. Terry buys a hammer and 50 nails from Di's DIY Shop. How much change does he get from £10?

   £[ ][ ].[ ][ ]

Di's DIY Shop	
Hammer	£2.50
Screwdriver	£4.50
10 nails	5p

8. June gets a 10% discount on everything except nails. How much does it cost June for a screwdriver, 30 nails and a hammer?

   £[ ][ ].[ ][ ]

9. A shop owner claims that the number of eggs he sold on Sunday is more than double the number he sold on Friday. He uses the chart below to back up his claim.

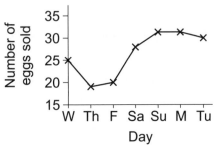

Why is the chart misleading? Circle the correct option.

A   It's hard to read the number of eggs sold.

B   The numbers don't start at 0.

C   The days don't start on Monday.

D   The shop is probably open for less time on a Sunday.

E   The numbers should go up in 1s or 2s.

Lucy is designing a logo. She makes two identical squares overlap.
The overlapping area is also a square, and is $\frac{1}{4}$ of the area of one of the bigger squares.

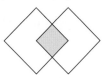

10. If the overlapping area is 9 cm², what is the area of the logo?

 cm²

11. What is the perimeter of the logo?

 cm

12. Sofia is giving out hats at her birthday party. She has five each of red, blue and green hats. The first person is given a blue hat, and the second person is given a green hat. What fraction of the remaining hats are red?
Circle the correct option.

A $\frac{4}{15}$ **C** $\frac{5}{13}$ **E** $\frac{1}{5}$ / 12

B $\frac{3}{13}$ **D** $\frac{1}{3}$

You have **10 minutes** to do this test. Work as quickly and accurately as you can.

1.   Use estimating to find 67 132 + 9840.78 + 812.5. Circle the correct option.

   A   17 368.78

   B   77 785.28

   C   166 352.3

   D   107 504.6

   E   2467.898

2.   In one season, a football team plays 60 matches. They draw 15% of their matches.
      How many matches does the team draw?

Mel goes fell-running one day. The graph below shows her distance from home.

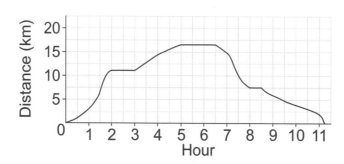

3.   Mel stops for a rest three times during her run. How long does she stop
      for the first time she has a rest? Circle the correct option.

   A   30 minutes   **C**   1 hour, 15 minutes   **E**   2 hours

   B   1 hour   **D**   1 hour, 30 minutes

4.   How long in total does Mel stop for during her run?

   [ ] hours, [ ][ ] minutes

14

5. 1 pint = 568 ml. A shop only sells milk in 1 pint cartons.
    How many cartons would you need to buy to get at least 6 litres of milk?

6. Mrs Rogers has stickers in different shapes. She has four square stickers,
    three triangle stickers and one heart sticker.

    What fraction of all her stickers are square? Circle the correct option.

    A $\frac{1}{8}$ **B** $\frac{1}{3}$ **C** $\frac{4}{9}$ **D** $\frac{3}{7}$ **E** $\frac{1}{2}$

7. A swimming pool has a diving board that is 350 cm above the surface
    of the water. The depth of the pool is 4.6 m. What is the distance,
    in metres, between the diving board and the bottom of the pool?

    ⬚⬚.⬚⬚ m

8. Shapes 1 and 2 are both made from identical regular hexagons.
    In Shape 1, the white space in the middle of the 3 hexagons has an area of 8 cm².

    Shape 1   Shape 2

    What is the area of the white space in the middle of the 6 hexagons in Shape 2?

    ⬚⬚ cm²

9. The test scores of Mr Colin's class are: 8, 21, 22, 13.
    What is the mean of these scores?

The diagram shows three angles on a straight line.

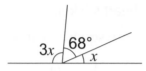

$3x$ $68°$ x

10. What is the size of angle x?

 °

11. A set of angles all the same size as angle x are put around a point.
     How many will fit without overlapping?

12. An unfair dice is rolled 36 times. The frequency that each number
     is rolled is shown in the pie chart.

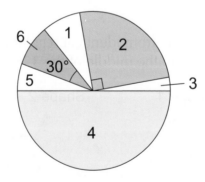

How many times does the dice land on an odd number? Circle the correct option.

    A   4

    B   6

    C   10

    D   12

    E   18

/ 12

16

Time for a break! These puzzles are a great way to practise your maths skills.

Moon, Star, Diamond, Circle

Each shape has a whole number value. Work out the value of each shape, and write the sum of each row and column in the box at the end.

$\newmoon$ = ____

$\bigstar$ = ____

$\blacklozenge$ = ____

$\bullet$ = ____

●	●	★	☽	□
☽	☽	☽	☽	36
★	◆	◆	★	18
★	☽	★	★	□
□	24	□	26	

Larry's Test

Larry's class does a test marked out of 100.
All of the scores except Larry's are shown here:

93, 88, 76, 44, 28, ?

What could Larry's score be if:

> the difference between the highest and lowest mark is 70? _____

> the most common score is 88? _____

> the mean score is 55? _____

17

You have **10 minutes** to do this test. Work as quickly and accurately as you can.

Kemi cuts the shapes below out of a piece of card.

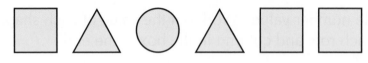

1. What is the ratio of quadrilaterals to non-quadrilaterals?
    Give your answer in its simplest form.

2. What fraction of the shapes are triangles? Circle the correct answer.

    A $^{1}/_{6}$
    B $^{1}/_{3}$
    C $^{2}/_{3}$
    D $^{5}/_{6}$
    E $^{1}/_{2}$

Daphne bought a painting at an antiques fair for £635.
She sold it one month later for £990.

3. How much profit did she make?

    £ ☐☐☐

4. Daphne uses her profit to buy blank DVDs. A box of 10 blank DVDs costs £5.
    How many blank DVDs can Daphne buy with her profit from selling the painting?

    ☐☐☐☐

5. A triangle has one angle of 51° and one angle of 72°.
What is the size of the triangle's third angle? Circle the correct answer.

   A 51°   **B** 72°   **C** 123°   **D** 57°   **E** 237°

6. The diagram shows the plan of a concrete platform.

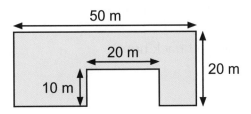

   What is the area of the platform?

 m²

Pete delivers newspapers. The table below shows the number of newspapers
he delivered each day during one week. One of the values is missing.

Mon	Tue	Wed	Thu	Fri	Sat	Sun
15	15	16	14		30	40

7. One in ten of the newspapers that Pete delivered that week were delivered
on Thursday. How many newspapers did he deliver on Friday?

8. What percentage of the whole week's newspapers did
Pete deliver on Saturday and Sunday combined?

   %

9. What was the mean number of newspapers he
delivered during the week shown?

10. Sophie sets off from home at 09:00 and jogs to the beach.
She then sits on a bench to rest, before jogging home again.
The graph below shows her distance from home during her journey.

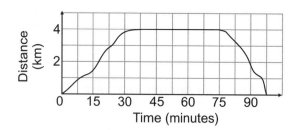

Circle the time that she sets off back home.

A   09:15

B   09:45

C   10:00

D   10:15

E   10:30

11. What is the sixth term in the sequence shown?

> 73, 71, 68, 64...

12. Mr Stark has two jars of sweets on his desk.
At the start of the week, each jar contains S sweets.
Mr Stark gives out 30 sweets during the course of the week.
Circle the expression that shows the total number of sweets
he has left at the end of the week.

A $30 - 2S$

B $2S - 30$

C $2 - S - 30$

D $30S - 2S$

E   28

/ 12

You have **10 minutes** to do this test. Work as quickly and accurately as you can.

1. A regular heptagon has sides of length 120 mm.
   What is the heptagon's perimeter?

    mm

2. Look at the diagram below.

   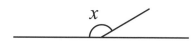

   Circle the best estimate for the size of angle x from the options below.

   A 100°   **B** 30°   **C** 230°   **D** 150°   **E** 330°

3. Mikael walks 740 m to the bus stop. He travels 2.5 km on the bus,
   and then walks another 120 m to his grandparents' house.
   How far has he travelled altogether, in km? Circle the correct answer.

   A 8.625 km   **B** 3.2 km   **C** 3.36 km   **D** 10.11 km   **E** 11.1 km

4. Patty is thinking of a number. She subtracts 6 and multiplies the result by 8.
   The result is 96. What number was she thinking of?

5. Brian buys a microwave from a supermarket for £70.
   The following week, the supermarket has a sale on electrical items.
   The microwave is reduced by 15%. How much money would
   Brian have saved if he had bought the microwave in the sale?

   £

21

6. The diagram shows a metal container in the shape of a cuboid.

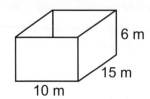

A builder pours cement into the container until it is ⅓ full.
What is the volume of cement in the container?

 m³

Mrs Ormerod asked the members of her class to name their favourite fish.
She recorded the results in the pie chart shown below.

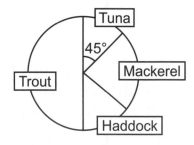

Four members of her class said that tuna was their favourite.

7. How many members of her class said that trout was their favourite?

8. How many said that either mackerel or haddock was their favourite?

9. The nth term in a sequence is given by the formula $20 - 4n$.
   What is the fifth term in the sequence?

The chart below shows the number of games won by
each player in a snooker tournament.

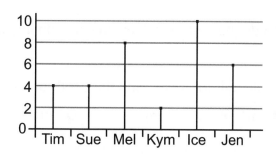

10. How many games were won by the person who came third
    in the tournament?

11. Which three players won a combined total number of games which was the same
    as the number of games won by Ice? Circle the correct answer.

    A   Tim, Sue and Mel

    B   Tim, Sue and Kym

    C   Sue, Mel and Kym

    D   Sue, Kym and Jen

    E   Mel, Kym and Jen

12. Simone and Callum are collecting conkers.
    Between them, they have collected a total of 29 conkers.
    Which of the following statements could be true? Circle the appropriate letter.

    A   Callum and Simone have each collected the same number of conkers.

    B   Callum has collected half as many conkers as Simone.

    C   Callum and Simone have each collected an even number of conkers.

    D   Callum and Simone have each collected an odd number of conkers.

    E   Callum has collected one more conker than Simone.

/ 12

You have **10 minutes** to do this test. Work as quickly and accurately as you can.

1. Circle the most suitable unit for measuring the depth of a well.

    A ml   **B** m²   **C** m   **D** m³   **E** mm

2. Sutinder wraps china cups in newspaper to store in his attic.
    One newspaper can wrap up 7 cups.
    How many newspapers does Sutinder need to wrap 161 cups?

Lizzy is drawing a table to show the number of sandwiches sold
in a cafe one lunchtime. She has filled in part of the table.

	White Bread	Brown Bread	**Total**
Cheese	12		
Turkey		16	**35**
Total			**80**

3. How many people chose cheese on brown bread?

4. What fraction of the people chose turkey on brown bread?
    Circle the correct answer.

    A ¹⁄₃   **B** ¹⁄₄   **C** ¹⁄₅   **D** ¹⁄₆   **E** ¹⁄₇

5. The shape below is reflected in the dotted mirror line.

The shape and its reflection together make a new shape.
Circle the name of the new shape.

A Pentagon   **C** Quadrilateral   **E** Heptagon

B Hexagon   **D** Octagon

The pictogram shows the number of albums owned by three music fans.

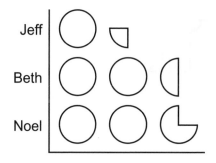

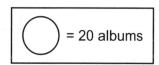

6. How many more albums does Noel own than Jeff?

7. $^3/_5$ of Beth's albums are heavy metal albums. How many albums is this?

8. Noel goes out and buys some new albums, so that he owns the same number
    of albums as Jeff and Beth put together.
    What is the mean number of albums owned by the three music fans now?

9. Look at the diagram shown below.

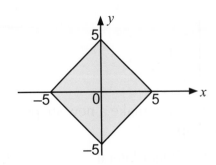

Which of these points is outside the shaded shape? Circle the correct answer.

A (–2, 0)   **B** (1, –1)   **C** (–5, 5)   **D** (0, –3)   **E** (4, 0)

10. The diagram below shows a rectangle attached to a right-angled triangle.

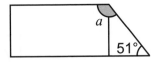

What is the size of angle *a*?

 °

Alicia is a taxi driver. She charges a flat rate of £4 per journey,
plus 80p per mile travelled.

11. Circle the formula which gives the amount, *A*, she would charge
     in pounds for a journey of *d* miles.

    A $A = 4d + 0.8$ **C** $A = 4.80d$ **E** $A = 4 + 0.8d$

    B $A = 4 + 80d$ **D** $A = 480 + d$

12. How much would she charge for a 15 mile journey?

£

/ 12

You have **10 minutes** to do this test. Work as quickly and accurately as you can.

The timetable below shows the times that a bus stops in five different towns.
The bus always runs exactly on time.

Flarehaven	Poolton	Leveleys	Livham	Vansdell
0900	0946	1021	1059	1132

1. Charles gets on the bus in Poolton.
    How long, in minutes, does it take him to get to Vansdell?

    ☐☐☐ minutes

2. Denise gets on the bus in one town. 35 minutes later, she gets off the
    bus in another town. Between which two towns did she travel?
    Circle the correct answer.

    A Poolton and Leveleys   **D** Leveleys and Livham

    B Leveleys and Vansdell   **E** Livham and Vansdell

    C Poolton and Livham

3. Circle the shape below which is not the same as the others when rotated.

    A 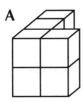   **C** 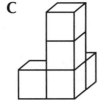   **E**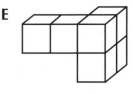

    B   **D**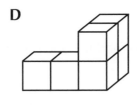

4. Which of the angles below is obtuse? Circle the correct answer.

A 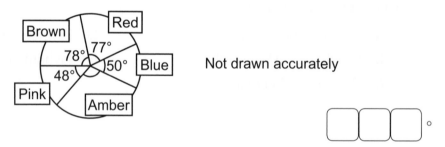 B   C   D   E

5. A stalactite increases in length at a rate of 2 mm per year. Circle the number
    of years it will take to increase from a length of 20 cm to a length of 29 cm.

    A 4.5 years   **D** 4500 years
    B 45 years   **E** 45 000 years
    C 450 years

6. What is the angle of the 'Amber' section in the pie chart shown?

    Brown Red 78° 77° 50° Blue 48° Pink Amber

    Not drawn accurately

    ⬜⬜⬜ °

A farmer uses 45 kg of hay to feed five horses for one day.

7. How many kilograms of hay would she need to feed 8 horses for one day,
    if each horse eats the same amount of hay?

    ⬜⬜⬜ kg

8. How many horses could she feed for one day with 135 kg of hay?

    ⬜⬜⬜

Six balls, labelled A-F, are placed in a hat. A number of people are asked to pick out a ball at random. The ball is then replaced. The graph shows the number of times each ball was picked.

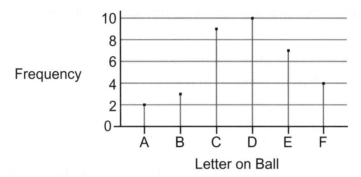

9.   What fraction of the people picked the ball marked 'D'? Circle the correct answer.

A $^3/_5$ **B** $^2/_7$ **C** $^4/_9$ **D** $^3/_7$ **E** $^7/_{10}$

10. Bethany is drawing a pie chart to show this data.
     What angle should she use for the 'E' sector?

11. Joan is stacking boxes in a pile. Each box is a cuboid with a height of 15 cm and a mass of 0.2 kg. Joan stacks the boxes to a total height of 240 cm.
     What is the total mass of the stack of boxes?

 kg

12. Raj is thinking of a number. He divides it by 2, subtracts 15, and then multiplies the result by 8. Which of the following expressions shows the result if the number he started with was x? Circle the correct answer.

     A $x \div 2 - 15 \times 8$
     B $(x - 15) \div 2 \times 8$
     C $x \times 8 \div 2 - 15$
     D $x \div (2 - 15 \times 8)$
     E $8(x \div 2 - 15)$

/ 12

You have **10 minutes** to do this test. Work as quickly and accurately as you can.

1. Ricky buys 3 bags of crisps for 37p each. He pays with a £2 coin.
    How much change does he receive, in pence?

 p

A quadrilateral has two sides of length 23 cm and two sides of length 30 cm.
It contains three angles of size 81°.

2. What is the quadrilateral's perimeter?

 cm

3. What is the size of the quadrilateral's fourth angle?

 °

George carries out a survey. He asks a group of people to say how many fizzy drinks
they each consumed during one week. The pie chart shows the results.

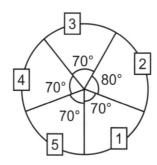

4. What was the most common response?
    Circle the correct answer.

    A 1   **B** 2   **C** 3   **D** 4   **E** 5   **F** 70

5. There were 36 people in the survey.
    How many of them only had 1 fizzy drink during that week?

6. Look at the sequence of patterns below.

Pattern 1   Pattern 2   Pattern 3   Pattern 4

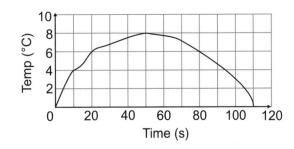

How many dots will there be in the sixth pattern?

The graph below shows how the temperature of a chemical changed over time during an experiment.

7. After how many seconds did the chemical reach its highest temperature?

 s

8. Jeffrey writes down the temperature of the chemical 10 seconds and 20 seconds after the start of the experiment.
What is the difference between the two temperatures he writes down?

°C

The table shows the finishing times, in seconds, of the runners in a 100 m sprint.

Dinah	Tabby	Pam	Debbie	Moirah	Jill	Summer
15.45	14.97	15.21	15.12	15.35	16.01	16.13

9.   Circle the option which correctly shows the first, second and third placed finishers.

   A   First Place: Tabby   Second Place: Pam   Third Place: Debbie
   B   First Place: Jill   Second Place: Debbie   Third Place: Summer
   C   First Place: Tabby   Second Place: Jill   Third Place: Summer
   D   First Place: Debbie   Second Place: Pam   Third Place: Moirah
   E   First Place: Tabby   Second Place: Debbie   Third Place: Pam

10. What was the time difference between the quickest
     and slowest finishing times?

The cost of hiring a floorboard sander from Sandra's Sanders is £60 per day.
There is also a one-off hire fee of £150, which covers the whole rental period.

11. Circle the expression which shows the total cost,
     in pounds, of hiring the sander for n days.

   A $60 + 150n$
   B $210n$
   C $210 + n$
   D $150 + 60n$
   E $150 \times 60n$

12. A rival company, Super Sanderz, charges a one-off fee of £60,
     plus £80 per day to hire the sander.

     Pat wants to hire a sander for four days.
     How much cheaper would it be to hire a sander from
     Super Sanderz than Sandra's Sanders?

/ 12

Time for a break! These puzzles are a great way to practise your maths skills.

Blackboard Blues

Look at the calculations written on the blackboard.

Can you add **one straight line** to each calculation to make them correct?

$$10 - 5 = 15$$
$$111 + 1 = 3$$
$$1 - 3 = 2$$
$$1 + 7 = 14$$
$$5 + 5 + 5 = 550$$

Hint: You can add the straight line to any part of the calculation — symbol or number.

Drawing Straws

The picture below shows nine identical straws arranged to make three equilateral triangles.

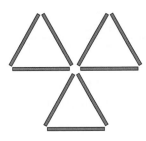

Starting with the shape shown, what is the minimum number of moves it would take to rearrange the straws into the following shapes?

- ■ Four equilateral triangles   _____ move(s)

- ■ Two equilateral triangles   _____ move(s)

- ■ One equilateral triangle   _____ move(s)

(Repositioning one straw counts as a move.)

33

You have **10 minutes** to do this test. Work as quickly and accurately as you can.

1. Which of these arrows is pointing to 1.24? Circle the correct answer.

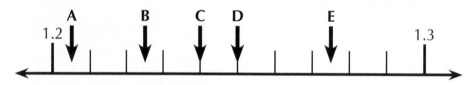

2. This map shows some of the rides at a funfair.

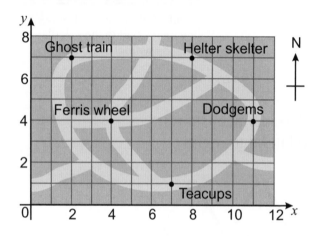

Craig stands at (7, 4), facing north. He turns 90° anticlockwise.
What can he see? Circle the correct answer.

> **A** Ghost train
> **B** Helter skelter
> **C** Ferris wheel
> **D** Dodgems
> **E** Teacups

3. Ellie buys four bags of flour for £1.20 each. She pays with a £10 note.
    How much change does she get?

    £ ⬚ . ⬚ ⬚

4. The diagram shows a parallelogram.

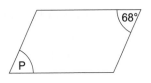

What is the size of angle P?

 °

5. This pie chart shows the results of a survey.
80 people were asked which of four milkshake flavours they prefer.

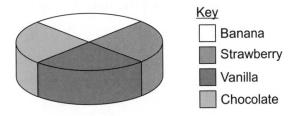

Key
☐ Banana
▨ Strawberry
■ Vanilla
☐ Chocolate

Why is the pie chart misleading? Circle the correct answer.

    A   100 people should have been questioned.

    B   The sections should be coloured to match the flavours.

    C   Only four flavours are included.

    D   The chart makes the vanilla section look more important than it should.

    E   The key does not list the flavours in alphabetical order.

6. Becky buys ten 330 ml cans of lemonade and two 1.5 litre bottles of cola.
How many litres of drinks does she buy in total?

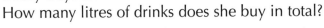  litres

7. Nina, David and Regina sold tickets for a concert. Nina sold 1289,
David sold 1455 and Regina sold 1606. How many tickets did they sell in total?

Harvey drew the net of a cube of side length 10 cm on a sheet of card, as shown below.

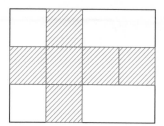

8.   What is the area of the original sheet of card?

 cm²

9.   What fraction of the sheet is used to make the net? Circle the correct option.

   A $^3/_5$ **C** $^1/_2$ **E** $^3/_4$
   B $^4/_{10}$ **D** $^1/_3$

10. The mean of five numbers is 180. Four of the numbers are
     155, 162, 190 and 198. What is the fifth number?

Alice is A years old. Barney is twice as old as Alice.
Charlene is 4 years younger than Barney.

11. Which of these expressions represents Charlene's age?
     Circle the correct answer.

     A $A - 2$ **C** $2A + 4$ **E** $2A - 4$
     B $4 - 2A$ **D** $2(A - 4)$

12. Charlene's grandad is three times as old as her.
     He is 78 years old. How old is Barney?

/ 12

You have **10 minutes** to do this test. Work as quickly and accurately as you can.

1. 1562 litres of a new brand of perfume costs £73 414 to make.
    How much does it cost to make 15.62 litres of the perfume, in pounds?

     £ ⬜⬜⬜⬜.⬜⬜

Martina makes the two shapes shown below using identical tiles.
The tiles are equilateral triangles.

Shape 1

Shape 2

2. Shape 1 has a perimeter of 30 cm. What is the perimeter of Shape 2?

     ⬜⬜ cm

3. Write the perimeter of Shape 2 to the perimeter of Shape 1
    as a ratio in its simplest form.

    ⬜⬜ : ⬜⬜

4. In a 'tallest sunflower' competition, the winning sunflower was 5.76 m tall.
    The shortest flower in the competition was 2.89 m shorter than the winner.

    How tall was the shortest sunflower in the competition? Circle the correct answer.

A	2.73 m	**C**	2.87 m	**E**	3.13 m
B	2.83 m	**D**	2.89 m		

5. Penny and Brian went apple picking.
Penny collected 1.7 kg of apples. Brian collected 1550 g of apples.

How many kilograms of apples did they collect between them?

$$\boxed{}\boxed{}.\boxed{}\boxed{}\boxed{}$$ kg

Cecilia, Paul and Art made 12 sandwiches.
Cecilia ate $^5/_{12}$ of the sandwiches. Paul ate $^1/_4$ of the sandwiches. Art ate the rest.

6. How many sandwiches did Art eat? Circle the correct answer.

   A 4   **B** 5   **C** 6   **D** 7   **E** 8

7. They also made 4 litres of lemonade. Cecilia drank 25% of the lemonade.
Paul and Art drank the rest. If Paul drank twice as much as Art, how much
did Art drink? Circle the correct answer.

   A   1 litres

   B   2 litres

   C   2.25 litres

   D   2.5 litres

   E   3 litres

8. This design has been made with identically-sized grey and white squares.

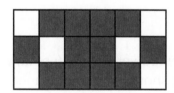

   How many lines of symmetry does the design have?

   $\boxed{}$

9. A group of friends won £6000 in a competition.
They shared the money equally, and each person received £750.

How many friends were there in the group? Circle the correct answer.

A 5 **B** 6 **C** 7 **D** 8 **E** 9

This graph shows the progress of a charity fundraising campaign.
The total amount raised since the start of the campaign was recorded at
the end of each week. They stopped when they reached their target of £4000.

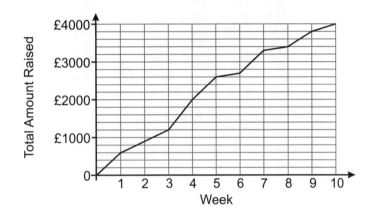

10. How much money was raised during the fourth week? Circle the correct answer.

A £400 **C** £800 **E** £2100

B £600 **D** £900

11. If each week they raised the same amount as they did in the first week,
after how many full weeks would they have passed their target?

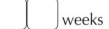 weeks

12. The first five numbers in a sequence are: 100, 98, 94, 88, 80.

What will the seventh number in the sequence be?

/ 12

You have **10 minutes** to do this test. Work as quickly and accurately as you can.

1. A group of people were asked which of six animals would make the best mascot for their local football team. The chart shows the results of the survey.

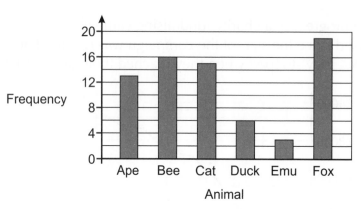

How many more people answered 'Ape' than answered 'Duck'?

Six competitors took part in a paper aeroplane throwing competition.
The tables below show the distance each competitor's aeroplane flew.

Name	Distance
Abigail	18.48 m
Alexei	17.89 m
Cooper	18.25 m

Name	Distance
Li	18.04 m
Dina	17.9 m
Zora	18.31 m

2. The competitors were ranked by their distance, from longest to shortest.
    Who threw the next longest distance after Cooper? Circle the correct answer.

    A Abigail   **C** Li   **E** Zora
    B Alexei   **D** Dina

3. The winner gets £5 for each metre their plane flew, rounded
    to the nearest metre. How much did the winner get?

    £ ☐☐☐

4. Bella's hens have laid 57 eggs. She puts the eggs into egg boxes.
   If each box holds six eggs, how many boxes will Bella need?

5. Clive buys 5.5 m of copper wire. He uses 75 cm of the wire.

   How much wire is left? Circle the correct answer.

   A   4.3 m

   B   4.55 m

   C   4.6 m

   D   4.75 m

   E   5.15 m

6. Amber buys a hat in a sale. The hat normally costs £18, but the price
   has been reduced by 10%. How much does the hat cost in the sale?

   £ ⬚⬚.⬚⬚

7. Rudy recorded the temperature in his garden five times during a single day.
   The temperatures he recorded were 14 °C, 24 °C, 27 °C, 27 °C and 18 °C.

   Which of the following statements is true? Circle the correct answer.

   A   The difference between the hottest and coldest temperatures was 24 °C.

   B   The maximum temperature was 24 °C.

   C   The third-coldest temperature was 24 °C.

   D   The most common temperature he recorded was 24 °C.

   E   The minimum temperature was 24 °C.

8. Jenny walked once around the perimeter of a rectangular field. In total, she
   walked 2650 m. The length of the field is 850 m. What is the width of the field?

   ⬚⬚⬚⬚ m

9. What is the size of angle x in the triangle below? Circle the correct answer.

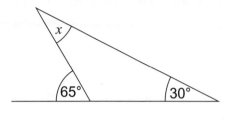

A 30° **B** 35° **C** 65° **D** 85° **E** 115°

10. $3m - 7 = 20$. What is the value of m?

$m = $ ☐☐

Lloyd draws the following sketch to show the coordinates of three corners of a rhombus.

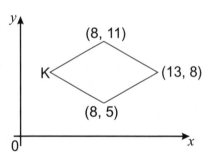

11. What are the coordinates of point K?

(☐☐ , ☐☐)

12. Lloyd then draws a horizontal line from K to (13, 8), splitting the rhombus into two triangles. He uses these triangles to find the area of the rhombus. What is the area he calculates? Circle the correct option.

A 8 **C** 30 **E** 64

B 16 **D** 56

/ 12

You have **10 minutes** to do this test. Work as quickly and accurately as you can.

1. Joel is collecting football stickers. There are 121 to collect, and so far
    he has collected 37. How many more stickers are there for him to collect?

2. How many acute angles are there inside a regular pentagon?

This pictogram shows the number of pupils in each of six classes in a school.

Class 1	●●●◤
Class 2	●●●●●◖
Class 3	●●●
Class 4	●●●●●
Class 5	●●◖
Class 6	●●●◖

Key
● = 4 pupils

3. The two smallest classes are combined for a school trip.
    How many pupils are there in the combined group?

4. ¹/₃ of the pupils in Class 4 get ill and can't go on the school trip.
    How many pupils from Class 4 do go on the trip?

5. Which of the following is equal to $^{23}/_5$?
Circle the correct answer.

   A 5.3   **B** 4.6   **C** 5.4   **D** 3.8   **E** 3.2

6. Joey starts watching a film at 14:45. The film lasts for 142 minutes.
What time will it be when the film ends? Give your answer in 24-hour clock format.

7. Harriet makes some purple paint by mixing 1.75 litres of red paint
with 480 ml of blue paint and 710 ml of white paint.

   How many litres of purple paint does she end up with? Circle the correct answer.

   A   2.94 litres
   B   1.365 litres
   C   2.79 litres
   D   3.24 litres
   E   2.59 litres

8. What is the volume of this cuboid?

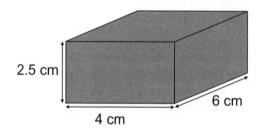

2.5 cm

4 cm

6 cm

⬚⬚⬚ cm³

9. Suzy divides a circle into four equally-sized sections. She then divides two of the sections in half. She uses her circle to create the spinner shown below.

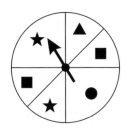

What fraction of the whole spinner is made up of star sections?
Circle the correct answer

A $^3/_8$ **B** $^1/_4$ **C** $^3/_4$ **D** $^1/_3$ **E** $^3/_5$

Joan went on holiday. On the second day she took 133 photos. On the third day she took 53 photos. On the fourth and final day she took as many photos as in the first 3 days put together.

10. In total, Joan took 400 photos during her holiday. What was the mean number of photos she took per day?

11. How many photos did she take during the first day?

12. The first four patterns in a sequence are shown below.

How many squares will there be in the eighth pattern in the sequence?

Test 14

10

You have **10 minutes** to do this test. Work as quickly and accurately as you can.

1. The parallelogram shown below is reflected in the mirror line.

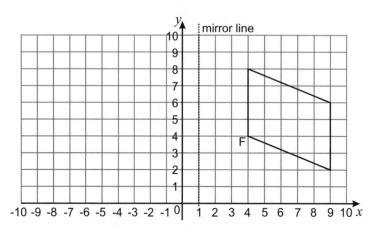

What are the coordinates of the reflection of point F? Circle the correct answer.

A   (–7, 4)   **C**   (–2, 4)   **E**   (2, –4)

B   (–4, 4)   **D**   (–4, –4)

2. What number is 9 less than –13? Circle the correct option.

A   –22   **B**   –4   **C**   4   **D**   6   **E**   22

Seats have been put out in a school hall, ready for a concert.
There are 9 rows of 10 seats and 8 rows of 15 seats.

3. How many seats have been set out in total?

4. The school has a total of 300 seats.
    What percentage of the seats have been set out?

A group of 60 people went on a coach trip. For their lunch, they each had a choice of cheese or ham sandwiches and a choice of an apple or a banana. This table shows the number of people who chose each option.

	Cheese	Ham	Total
Apple		8	
Banana	15		
Total		28	60

5.   How many people chose a cheese sandwich and an apple?

6.   What fraction of the total number of people had a banana?
      Circle the correct option.

      A $^5/_{12}$ **C** $^9/_{10}$ **E** $^2/_3$
      B $^7/_{12}$ **D** $^{30}/_{40}$

7.   Josh is buying a fish tank for his four new tropical fish. Which of the following would be the most sensible choice for the capacity of the fish tank? Circle the correct option.

      A   15 ml   **C**   500 ml   **E**   150 000 000 ml
      B   150 ml   **D**   150 000 ml

8.   The programmes shown on a TV channel over a 24-hour period were divided into seven categories. This pie chart shows the proportion of each type of programme.

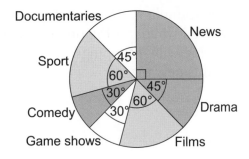

      How many hours of sport were shown?

      [ ] hours

9. For which of the following pairs of dice do both of the faces shown have the same number of lines of symmetry? Circle the correct answer.

A

B

C

D

E

10. Joseph is thinking of a number. He says, "the number is a factor of 66, it is greater than 5, and it is prime".
What number is he thinking of?

11. What is the area of this shape?

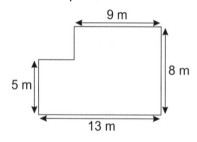

9 m

8 m

5 m

13 m

☐☐☐ m²

12. A pizza restaurant uses the formula $P = 5 + 0.4t$ to work out P, the price in pounds of a pizza where t is the number of toppings.
The chef creates a new recipe with 4 toppings.
What will be the price of this new pizza?

£☐☐.☐☐

/ 12

Puzzles 3

Time for a break! These puzzles are a great way to practise your maths skills.

Whose House?

The picture shows five houses on the same street.

Anna, Bex, Carrie, Don and Edgar each live in one of these houses.

Use the clues below to work out who lives in each house.

- Bex lives in a house with a prime number on either side.

- Anna lives in a house which is a multiple of 3.

- Edgar lives next door to Bex.

- Carrie lives next door to a house with a square number.

Number	Name
19	
21	
23	
25	
27	

Crazy Computer

Captain Calculator's Space Computer has developed a fault.

It has replaced the digits 0-9 with symbols.

Using the sums below, work out which symbol matches each digit.

Then find the code Captain Calculator needs to reset the computer.

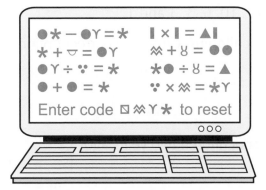

⦂ =		Υ =		❘ =	
▽ =		✶ =		◻ =	
● =	1	♒ =			
▲ =		୪ =			

Code =				

(10)

You have **10 minutes** to do this test. Work as quickly and accurately as you can.

1. Richard records the colours of all the cars he sees one day in a pie chart.

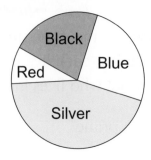

What is the most common colour that Richard sees? Circle the correct option.

A Black

B Blue

C Silver

D Red

E Cannot tell

2. Chelsea has 1.5 kg of sugar. She divides it into equal piles that each weigh 75 g.
    How many piles of sugar can Chelsea make?

The ages of Mr Mann's six grandchildren are 13, 10, 6, 3, 3 and 1.

3. What is the mean age of Mr Mann's grandchildren? Circle the correct option.

A	36	**C**	6	**E**	5.5
B	4	**D**	12		

4. What was the mean age of Mr Mann's grandchildren two years ago?

5.   What is the size of angle x? The diagram is not drawn accurately.

133° x

⬚⬚⬚ °

6.   A lorry can hold 4096 boxes of chocolate. Each box weighs 807 g.
      What is the combined weight, in grams, of all the boxes of chocolate?
      Circle the correct option.

| **A** | 1 886 244 | **C** | 5 589 636 | **E** | 9 367 820 |
| **B** | 3 305 472 | **D** | 5 987 502 | | |

Below is a coordinate grid. The units are in centimetres.

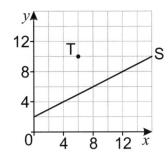

7.   The line L is parallel to the line S and goes through point T.
      What are the coordinates of the point where L meets the y-axis?

(⬚ , ⬚)

8.   A horizontal line and a vertical line are drawn through point T.
      What is the area of the triangle formed by these two lines and line S?

 cm²

9. Cally is thinking of a number. She doubles it, adds four and then doubles it again. She ends up with 44. What number did Cally start with?

10. A rectangular garden has width x m. Its length is 5 m more than its width, as shown, and its area is 126 m².

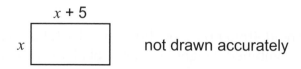

not drawn accurately

Which equation shows this information? Circle the correct option.

A $x(x + 5) = 126$

B $x + x + 5 = 126$

C $2 \times (2x + 5) = 126$

D $(x - 5)x = 126$

E $x + 5 = 126$

11. There are 240 squirrels in a wood. $\frac{1}{3}$ of them are not grey. Of those that aren't grey, 15% are black. How many black squirrels are there in the wood?

12. John has a bag of 25 sweets, $\frac{1}{5}$ of which are cherry. He picks a cherry sweet out of the bag and eats it. What fraction of the remaining sweets are cherry? Circle the correct option.

A $\frac{5}{24}$

B $\frac{1}{4}$

C $\frac{1}{6}$

D $\frac{4}{25}$

E $\frac{24}{25}$

/ 12

(10)

You have **10 minutes** to do this test. Work as quickly and accurately as you can.

1. Which of the following is a hexagon? Circle the correct option.

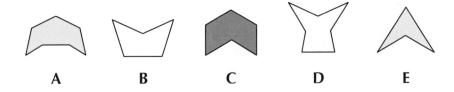

A   B   C   D   E

2. A snail travels a distance of 0.5 cm every second.
   How long would it take the snail to travel 1 metre?

   ☐ minute(s) ☐☐ second(s)

3.

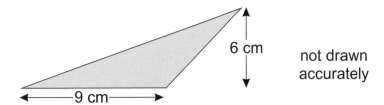

6 cm

9 cm

not drawn
accurately

What is the area of the triangle above? Circle the correct option.

A   30 cm²
B   36 cm²
C   54 cm²
D   27 cm²
E   18 cm²

Wayne and Linda work at a guitar shop. The number of guitars they each sold in one week is shown in a line graph.

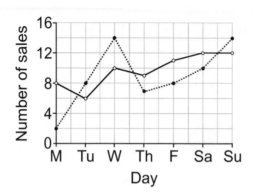

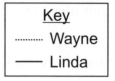

Key
.... Wayne
——— Linda

4. What is the difference in the number of guitars sold by Wayne and Linda on Friday?

5. The price of each guitar that Wayne and Linda sold on Monday was £185.45. How much money did they take on Monday from the guitar sales?

6. 459 × 6626 = 3 041 334

What is 45.9 × 66.26? Circle the correct option.

   A   3.041334
   B   30.41334
   C   304.1334
   D   3041.334
   E   30413.34

7. A shop sells 500 g bags of pasta for £1.60, and 1.5 kg bags of pasta for £3.60. Louise needs 3 kg of pasta for a buffet. How much money could she save by buying the 1.5 kg bags?

£ ☐ . ☐☐

8.

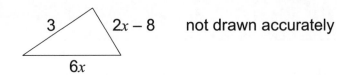

not drawn accurately

What is the perimeter of the triangle above? Circle the correct option.

A $9x + 5$ **C** $8x - 5$ **E** $8x + 5$

B $4x + 5$ **D** $5x - 2$

9. A sequence starts 1, 2, 4, 7, 11, ...
    What are the next two terms in the sequence?

10. Which of the following gives the smallest answer? Circle the correct option.

A 10% of 158

B $^1/_2$ of 30

C 0.1×100

D $^2/_3$ of 24

E 20% of 90

The sum of the angles in a polygon can be found using the expression $180(x - 2)$, where x is the number of sides of the polygon.

11. What is the sum of the angles in an octagon?

12. The sum of the angles in a shape is 1800°.
     How many sides does the polygon have?

/ 12

You have **10 minutes** to do this test. Work as quickly and accurately as you can.

1. The masses of Sarah's pets are listed below.

    23.5 kg, 8.11 kg, 200 g, 1.1 kg

    What is the difference, in kilograms, between her heaviest and lightest pets?

     kg

2.

    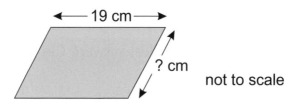

    not to scale

    The perimeter of the parallelogram is 62 cm.
    What is the length of the shorter side?

     cm

A cup holds 256 ml of water and a bathtub holds 189.4 litres of water.

3. How many cups could you fill from the water in a full bathtub?
    Circle the correct option.

A 739	**C** 1165	**E** 341
B 625	**D** 1373	

4. The bath drains at a rate of 5 litres per minute. How long does it take for a
    full bath to drain completely? Round your answer up to the nearest whole minute.

    minutes

A poster sold at a museum is a copy of a painting, but at 75% the size of the original.

5. If the poster is 60 cm wide, how wide is the original painting?
    Circle the correct option.

    A   45 cm   **C**   75 cm   **E**   90 cm

    B   50 cm   **D**   80 cm

6. The museum also sells a postcard version of the painting. It is $^1/_{20}$ of the price of
    the poster. The poster costs £18.00. How much does the postcard cost?

    £ ⬚⬚ . ⬚⬚

7. Andy records the number of CDs four of his teachers have in their CD collection.

Teacher	Number of CDs
Miss Elliot	◎ ◎ ◎ ◎ ◎ ◗
Mrs Robinson	◎ ◎ ◎ ◖
Miss Jackson	◎ ◎ ◗
Miss McKenzie	◎ ◎ ◎ ◎ ◎

◎ = ? CDs

There are 34 CDs in Mrs Robinson's collection and Miss McKenzie's collection
combined. What number should replace the '?' in the key?

⬚⬚

8. A postman starts his deliveries at 4:20 am. He delivers to two houses per minute,
    and there are 200 houses on his route. If he has a 20 minute break during
    his round, what time will he finish?

    ⬚⬚ : ⬚⬚ am

9. What is 7892.3216 rounded to the nearest thousandth? Circle the correct option.

    A   8000
    B   7900
    C   7892.322
    D   7892.321
    E   7892.32

10. On Monday, Miss Leigh marks 50 papers. Each day after that, she marks 5 fewer papers than the day before. How many papers does she mark from Monday to Friday? Circle the correct option.

    A   250
    B   225
    C   200
    D   175
    E   150

11. The diagram below shows three points joined together to form two sides of a shape.

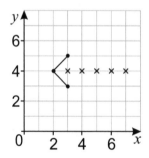

    Frank joins the two sides to each of the five crosses in turn, to form five different shapes. How many irregular quadrilaterals are formed as he does this?

12. A rectangular sports pitch needs its perimeter repainting.
    Joanna can paint x m of the perimeter every minute.
    The pitch is $2x$ m wide, and the length is twice the width.
    How long does it take Joanna to paint the perimeter of the pitch?

    minutes

    / 12

You have **10 minutes** to do this test. Work as quickly and accurately as you can.

1. How many factors of 30 are also factors of 15? Circle the correct option.

   A 0   **C** 2   **E** 4
   B 1   **D** 3

The table shows the temperature of four cities one day.

City	Temperature (°C)
Oslo	−9
Helsinki	−16
Paris	−1
Rome	11

2. What is the difference between the warmest and coldest temperatures shown?

   ☐☐ °C

3. On the day that these temperatures were recorded, Helsinki was 18.3 °C warmer than its coldest ever temperature. What was its lowest ever temperature?

   −☐☐.☐ °C

4. Ellie completes a 400 m race in 80 seconds. It takes Amy 25% longer than Ellie to complete the race. How many seconds does it take Amy to complete the race?

   ☐☐☐ seconds

5. A rectangle has side lengths 4 m and 250 cm. What is its area in m²?

     m²

6. There are approximately 35.274 ounces in 1 kg. There are approximately
    6.35 kg in 1 stone. Circle the number of ounces in 1 stone.

    A 5.55   **C** 224   **E** 828
    B 176   **D** 0.18

7. A group of people were asked to choose which type of holiday they would like
    to go on next, out of six different options. The results are given in a bar chart.

    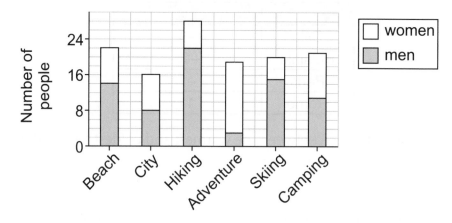

    How many more men than women chose skiing?

8. Which of the following shapes has the greatest number of lines of symmetry?
    Circle the correct option.

    A Isosceles triangle
    B Kite
    C Scalene triangle
    D Rectangle
    E Equilateral triangle

9. Four identical squares with sides of length 5 cm are put together to make a shape where each 'step' from one square to the next is 1 cm.

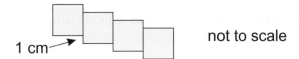

1 cm

not to scale

What is the perimeter of this shape?

 cm

On the coordinate grid is a line and five points labelled A to E.

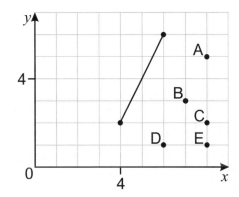

10. Circle the only labelled point that doesn't form a right-angled triangle or isosceles triangle when joined with the two end points of the line.

11. Two triangles are made — the first one has corners B, D and E, the second one has corners A, D and E. How many times greater is the area of the second triangle than that of the first triangle?

12. In a sequence of dots, there are $\frac{1}{2}n(n + 1)$ dots in the nth pattern. What is the pattern number for the pattern made up of 28 dots? Circle the correct option.

    A 5   C 11   E 16
    B 7   D 15

/ 12

You have **10 minutes** to do this test. Work as quickly and accurately as you can.

1.   A new road is exactly 236 515 cm long. How long is the road in kilometres?
     Circle the correct option.

    A   0.236515 km

    B   2.36515 km

    C   23.6515 km

    D   236.515 km

    E   2365.15 km

2.   Circle the shape below which has a different number of
     lines of symmetry to the others.

   A   **B**   **C**   **D**   **E**

3.   The volume of a triangular prism is: | area of triangular face × length |

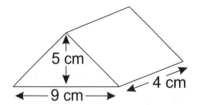

                          not to scale

What is the volume of the triangular prism above?

 cm³

4. What is $2140 \times 1.1 + 0.9 \times 2140$?

5. The times of five runners who took part in a 200 m race are shown in the table.

Runner	Paula	Andrew	Mohammed	Jenni	Thomas
Time (s)	29.89	47.82	46.95	31.59	28.94

What was the time difference between the fastest and
slowest finishers?

 s

6. How many common multiples of 5 and 6 are there between 80 and 100?

The pie chart shows the favourite type of book of 60 people in a book club.

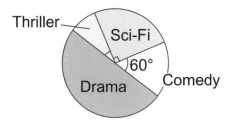

7. How many people said that comedy was their favourite type of book?

8. What fraction of the book club said their favourite type of book is a thriller?
Circle the correct option.

    A $\frac{1}{8}$ **C** $\frac{1}{10}$ **E** $\frac{1}{15}$

    B $\frac{1}{9}$ **D** $\frac{1}{12}$

9. The Number Cruncher uses a formula to turn one number into another.

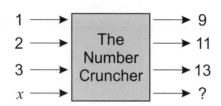

When you put x into The Number Cruncher, what comes out?
Circle the correct option.

    A $9x$ **C** $2x + 7$ **E** $5x + 1$

    B $x + 8$ **D** $5x + 4$

Gregory ploughs a field at a rate of 200 m² per minute,
and trims hedgerows at a rate of 50 m per minute.

10. If he starts ploughing a 300 m × 400 m rectangular field at 9:00 am,
what time will he finish?

 pm

11. The perimeter of the field is a hedgerow. He starts trimming
the hedgerow immediately after finishing ploughing.
What time will he finish trimming the hedgerow?

 pm

12. Keith makes a sequence where every term is greater than the previous term.
To find a term, Keith multiplies the previous term by itself. Which of the following
numbers could Keith have started with? Circle the correct option.

    A   −1   **C**   0.5   **E**   2

    B   0   **D**   1

/ 12

Time for a break! These puzzles are a great way to practise your maths skills.

The Chess Tournament

The leaderboard in a chess tournament is shown here:

> ## Leaderboard
> 1st Aaron
> 2nd Mohammed
> 3rd Hayley
> 4th Emma
> 5th Andrew

Some of the players are a bit fussy
about who they next play:

Emma says, *"I'll only play against another girl."*

Hayley says, *"I won't play against anyone whose name begins with A."*

Andrew says, *"If I'm not playing against Mohammed, I'm not playing."*

Two people next to each other on the leaderboard
can't play each other. Who is playing in the next game?

_____ against _____

Pete's Pieces of Pizza

Pete has some pizzas and a pizza cutter that cuts in a straight line.
He makes one cut in Pizza 1, two cuts in Pizza 2, and so on.

Pizza 1	Pizza 2	Pizza 3	Pizza 4

2 pieces   4 pieces   7 pieces   ☐ pieces

Draw cuts onto Pizza 3 to give 7 pieces. (They don't have to be the same size.)
Fill in the box with the maximum number of pieces Pete can make from Pizza 4.

Is there a pattern in the number of pieces that Pete can make?
How many pieces can he make from Pizza 5 and Pizza 6?

Pizza 5 = ☐ pieces   Pizza 6 = ☐ pieces

    65

You have **10 minutes** to do this test. Work as quickly and accurately as you can.

1. An equilateral triangle has a side length of 4.5 mm. What is its perimeter?

 . mm

2. Athena is shopping for bargains at a car boot sale.
    She buys four items from the table shown. She spends £14 in total.

Tea Set	Hat	Phone	Glove	Book
£4.00	£3.20	£6.00	£2.00	£0.80

Which four items did she buy?

A   Tea Set, Hat, Phone, Glove

B   Hat, Phone, Glove, Book

C   Tea Set, Phone, Glove, Book

D   Tea Set, Hat, Phone, Book

E   Tea Set, Hat, Glove, Book

3. Robert has a pile of identical equilateral triangle tiles.
    He places tiles next to each other to make different shapes,
    without the tiles overlapping.

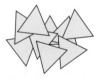

    Which of these shapes can he not make using the tiles? Circle the correct option.

A   Triangle   **C**   Parallelogram   **E**   Trapezium

B   Rectangle   **D**   Hexagon

4. A cardboard box weighs 150 g. 24 bags of crisps, each weighing 30 g,
    are put into the box. What is the total weight of a box filled with 24 bags of crisps?

     g

5. The bar chart below shows the numbers of apples and bananas
    sold in a grocer's over a period of five months.

    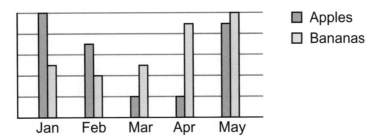

    Which month had the greatest difference between the number of apples
    and the number of bananas sold? Circle the correct answer.

    A   January   **C**   March   **E**   May
    B   February   **D**   April

6. The temperature in Nina's cellar is 8 °C at noon. The temperature in her cellar
    drops at a steady rate of 1 °C every 30 minutes over the course of the afternoon.
    What is the temperature in her cellar at 16:30? Circle the correct answer.

    A   –1 °C   **C**   –4 °C   **E**   0 °C
    B   –2 °C   **D**   1 °C

7. Siobhan starts at 50 and counts back in steps of 12.
    Which of these numbers will she count? Circle the correct answer.

    A   0   **C**   2   **E**   4
    B   1   **D**   3

8. Trevor has some square cards, all with the same side length.
He uses them to make the shape shown. Some of the cards are cut in half.

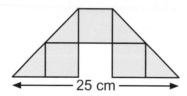

-------- 25 cm --------

What is the area of his shape?

 cm²

Jasmine is on a fishing trip. The mean number of fish she catches each
day over the first four days is 7. On the fifth day, she catches 2 fish.

9. What is the mean number of fish she catches over the five days?

10. Five of the fish she caught during the first 5 days were salmon. What fraction of
the fish she caught over this time were salmon? Circle the correct answer.

A $^5/_{28}$	**C** $^1/_6$	**E** $^5/_7$
B $^1/_5$	**D** $^2/_{15}$	

The diagram shows an L-shaped box.

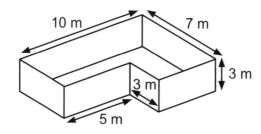

10 m   7 m

3 m

3 m

5 m

11. What is the volume of the box?

 m³

12. A lid is made to fit on top of the box. Each square metre
of the lid weighs 50 kg. What is the weight of the lid?

 kg

/ 12

68

You have **10 minutes** to do this test. Work as quickly and accurately as you can.

At work, Jordi makes himself a cup of tea every hour. Sally makes herself a cup of tea every hour and a half. They both make a cup of tea when they get to work at 09:00.

1. What time will they next both make a cup of tea at the same time?

2. They both leave work at 17:30. What is the total number of cups of tea that Jordi and Sally make in one day?

3. A strip of patterned cloth costs 5p per centimetre.

How much does the strip of cloth shown cost? Circle the correct answer.

A	£0.84	**C**	£4.00	**E**	£8.40
B	£0.42	**D**	£4.20		

4. What number will correctly complete the following calculation?

$$38 + 38 + 38 + 38 = 8 \times \underline{}$$

5. A block of butter has a mass of 500 g and costs 99p. Tina buys 6 kg of butter.
    How much does this cost her?

    £☐☐.☐☐

6. There are 50 packets of crisps on a shelf. 10% are ready salted, $^1/_5$ are cheese
    and pickle, 10 are prawn cocktail, and the rest are roast chicken.
    What is the most common crisp flavour on the shelf? Circle the correct answer.

    A   Ready salted

    B   Cheese and pickle

    C   Prawn cocktail

    D   Roast chicken

    E   Impossible to tell

7. The graph shown converts Cumberland Pounds to Westmorland Dollars.

    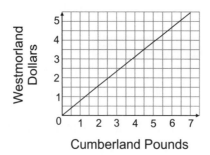

    Nadine converts 4.50 Cumberland Pounds into Westmorland Dollars.
    How many Westmorland Dollars does she receive? Circle the correct answer.

    A   2.50   **C**   3.25   **E**   5.75
    B   3.50   **D**   4.50

8. Henry and Harriet have 67 racing pigeons between them.
    Harriet has 13 more than Henry. How many racing pigeons does Harriet have?

    ☐☐

9. The diagram shows the lines *AB* and *PQ*. *AB* is perpendicular to *PQ*.

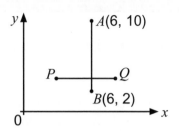

Which of these could be the coordinates of *P* and *Q*? Circle the correct answer.

A *P*(3, 3) and *Q*(8, 8)   **D** *P*(4, 2) and *Q*(8, 4)

B *P*(2, 4) and *Q*(7, 2)   **E** *P*(3, 3) and *Q*(7, 4)

C *P*(3, 3) and *Q*(8, 3)

Look at the diagram shown below.

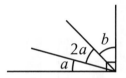

not drawn
accurately

10. Circle the expression which correctly describes the angles shown.

A $a + b = 90°$ **C** $2a + b = 90°$ **E** $3a + b = 180°$

B $3a + b = 45°$ **D** $3a + b = 90°$

11. Charmon measures angle *a* to be 18°. What is the size of angle *b*?

12. Zoe is carrying out a survey to find out what people's favourite take-away meal is.
     40% of the people she asked said 'kebab'. She draws a pie chart to show the
     results of the survey. What size angle should she use for the 'kebab' sector?

/ 12

You have **10 minutes** to do this test. Work as quickly and accurately as you can.

1. The number of people who voted for the winner in a reality TV series was two hundred thousand, five hundred and three. What is this in figures?

2. The bar chart below shows the numbers of different types of vehicle parked at a service station car park.

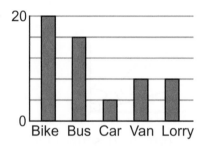

Which two types of vehicle had a combined total which was the same as the total for 'Bike'? Circle the correct answer.

A Bus and Van	**C** Bus and Car	**E** Van and Lorry
B Car and Van	**D** Car and Lorry	

In a shop, each banana costs 18p. Connor buys as many bananas as he can afford.

3. Connor has £2. How many bananas does he buy?

4. The mean mass of each banana that Connor buys is 120 g.
    What is the total mass of the bananas that Connor buys?

 g

5. Graeme pours some water into a 500 ml beaker, as shown.

Circle the best estimate for the amount of water in the beaker.

A   100 ml   **C**   5 ml   **E**   1000 ml

B   250 ml   **D**   450 ml

6. Find the area of the shape shown.

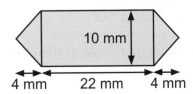

10 mm

4 mm   22 mm   4 mm

⬜⬜⬜ mm²

7. During the first six days of one week, Scott drove a total of 467 miles.
    His mean distance driven each day over the full seven-day week was 70 miles.
    How many miles did he drive on the seventh day?

⬜⬜⬜ miles

8. Donna is training for a marathon. Each week, she increases the distance
    she runs. In week 1, she runs 4 miles. In week 2, she runs 6 miles.
    In week 3, she runs 8 miles. She continues in this sequence.

    In which week will Donna run 26 miles?

Week ⬜⬜

9. What fraction of all the faces on a fair six-sided dice show a number which is a factor of 10? Circle the correct answer.

    A $\frac{1}{6}$ **C** $\frac{2}{3}$ **E** $\frac{1}{2}$

    B $\frac{1}{3}$ **D** $\frac{5}{6}$

Ronny has four rectangular tiles of size 8 cm × 3 cm and four square tiles with sides of 6 cm. He arranges them to make the pattern shown.

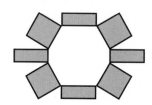

10. What is the perimeter of the octagonal hole at the centre of the shape?

 cm

11. The tiles cost 10p per square centimetre. How much does it cost Ronny to make the pattern? Circle the correct option.

    A   £24   **C**   £20   **E**   £14

    B   £40   **D**   £36

12. Kylie is mixing red and yellow paint to get the correct shade of tangerine. For every 0.75 litres of red paint, she uses 2.25 litres of yellow paint. She needs a total of 12 litres of paint to decorate her kitchen and bathroom. How many litres of red paint should she buy?

 litre(s)

/ 12

You have **10 minutes** to do this test. Work as quickly and accurately as you can.

1. The spinner shown is split into five different lettered sections.

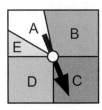

The pointer is turned 270° clockwise from its position shown in
the diagram. Which letter is it now pointing to?

Jimi is at an amusement arcade. He gets a £5 note changed into coins. He receives
five 50 pence pieces and ten 20 pence pieces. The rest is made up of 10 pence pieces.

2. How many 10 pence pieces does he receive?

3. After a while, Jimi has spent $^4/_5$ of the 50 pence pieces that he received.
    How much is this?

£ ☐ . ☐ ☐

4. Theo set off from home at 10:53 and drove to his parents' house.
    His journey took 2 hours and 42 minutes.
    What time did he arrive at his parents' house? Circle the correct answer.

    A   12:42   **C**   13:35   **E**   13:21

    B   14:25   **D**   12:35

5. Juliet is buying a coat in the sales. The sales prices of the coat in
    five different shops are given below. Circle the lowest sales price.

    A   50% of £80   **C**   ⁴/₁₀ of £80   **E**   £32.75
    B   £38   **D**   ¹/₂ of £80

6. Which of the following is the most suitable unit for measuring the distance
    between two cities? Circle the correct answer.
    A   km   **C**   cm   **E**   m²
    B   mm   **D**   m

7. Darius is washing cars. He earns £3 for every car he washes.
    The table shows the number of cars he washes during one week.

Day	Mon	Tue	Wed	Thu	Fri
Number of Cars	5	4	6	7	8

    What was the mean amount he earned per day during this week?

    £

The diagram shows a plastic box and a metal cube.

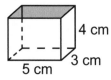

8. How many of the cubes will fit inside the box?

9. The box is extended in one direction so that it can fit 1 extra metal cube inside.
    The minimum amount of space is added. How much does the volume increase by?

    cm³

10. Leo records the eye colours of all the members of his cycling club.
He displays his results in the chart shown below.

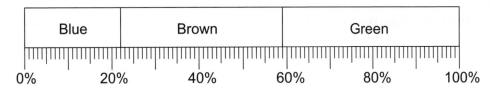

What percentage of his cycling club has brown eyes?

 %

11. David plots the points $A(-5, 5)$ and $B(5, -5)$ on a coordinate grid.
He joins them up to form the diagonal line AB. AB passes through the origin $(0, 0)$.
Circle the point below which is not on the line AB.

   A $(1, -1)$
   B $(-1, 1)$
   C $(2, 2)$
   D $(-2, 2)$
   E $(3, -3)$

12. The shape below is a parallelogram.

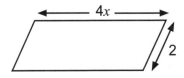

Circle the expression that gives the shape's perimeter.

   A $8x$
   B $4x + 2$
   C $8x + 2$
   D $8x + 4$
   E $6x$

/ 12

⏱ **10**

You have **10 minutes** to do this test. Work as quickly and accurately as you can.

1. Look at the shape below.

The shape is turned 90° anticlockwise. Circle the resulting shape.

A   **B**   **C**   **D**   **E**

2. Steve creates a sequence using the rule 'multiply the previous number by 3, then subtract 2 from the result'. Circle Steve's sequence from the options below.

    A   1, 2, 4...
    B   2, 4, 10...
    C   2, 4, 8...
    D   3, 9, 27...
    E   3, 7, 18...

3. The price list for a barber's shop is shown below.

One weekend, Gavin does 10 buzz cuts, 5 flat tops and 4 mohawks.
He earns £144. How much does Gavin charge for a mohawk?

£ ☐☐.☐☐

Two equilateral triangles each have a perimeter of 45 cm.
Toby joins them together as shown, to create a rhombus.

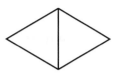

4.   What is the perimeter of Toby's rhombus?

 cm

5.   How many more rhombuses does Toby need to make so
     that they will fit together to make a regular hexagon?

6.   The graph shows the number of fish caught when using
     two different brands of fishing rod on a fishing trip.

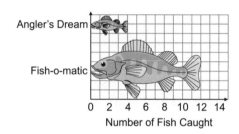

     Angler's Dream

     Fish-o-matic

     0   2   4   6   8   10 12 14
         Number of Fish Caught

     Why is the graph misleading? Circle the correct statement.

     A   It is impossible to catch 12 fish in one day.
     B   Not everyone likes fishing.
     C   The area for Fish-o-matic is more than 3 times the area for Angler's Dream.
     D   The horizontal axis values don't increase evenly.
     E   Only two brands of rod were tested.

7.   Rose is thinking of a number. Her number rounded to the nearest 10 is 1110.
     Circle the smallest number she could be thinking of.

     A   1110   **C**   1105   **E**   1104
     B   1100   **D**   1115

8. Rhoda is drawing a pictogram to show the number of eggs laid
    by her hens each month. She uses the key shown below.

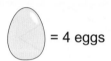 = 4 eggs

In January, her hens laid 35 eggs. How many egg pictures should
she use in the pictogram for January? Circle the correct answer.

A 10	**C** $8\frac{1}{2}$	**E** $8\frac{3}{4}$
B 9	**D** $7\frac{1}{4}$	

9. Find the size of angle x, shown below.

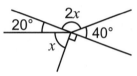

 °

10. Shirley is making a cottage pie. She usually uses 450 g of mince for 5 people.
    Today she is cooking for 8 people. How many grams of mince does she need?

 g

Gina has a collection of stamps. One fifth of all her stamps are from Britain,
one third are from France, and one quarter are from Sweden.

11. Which of the following could be the number of stamps in Gina's collection?
    Circle the correct answer.

A 50	**C** 30	**E** 20
B 40	**D** 60	

12. She sells some of her collection for £31.25, which is two and a half times
    the face value. What is the face value?

£

/ 12

Time for a break! This puzzle is a great way to practise your maths skills.

Maths Crossword

Use the clues given to complete the crossword.
One of the clues has been done for you.

[Crossword grid with cells. Filled in cells show:]
2. M
6. A
   S
   S

Across

1. A quadrilateral with one pair of parallel sides.
4. The number of sides in a quadrilateral.
6. Using letters to represent numbers. $2x + 1$
8. An eight-sided shape.
9. A 3D shape with triangular faces that meet at a point.
12. A three-sided shape.
15. A 3D shape with the same face at both ends.
17. An angle between 0° and 90°.
21. The top half of a fraction.
22. A 2D shape that folds to create a 3D shape.
23. A circular graph that shows the proportions of different values. (2 words)
24. A triangle with no equal sides or angles.
25. Two lines that will never meet.

Down

2. An amount measured in g or kg.
3. A number which divides exactly into another number.
5. A 2D shape with 4 equal sides and 2 pairs of parallel sides.
7. The order of operations.
8. An angle between 90° and 180°.
9. A chart that uses symbols.
10. The bottom half of a fraction.
11. A shape with sides of equal length and equal angles.
13. A triangle with two equal sides and two equal angles.
14. The units used to measure angles.
15. A number which only has itself and 1 as factors.
16. Average found by adding and dividing.
18. 100 cm.
19. The space in a 3D shape.
20. The space in a 2D shape.

You have **10 minutes** to do this test. Work as quickly and accurately as you can.

1.   A sequence begins 55, 45, 35, ... What is the fifth term in the sequence?

2.   A fair spinner numbered 1-6 is spun.

What fraction of the spinner is numbered with a factor of 12?
Circle the correct answer.

    A $\frac{1}{2}$ **B** $\frac{1}{6}$ **C** $\frac{5}{6}$ **D** $\frac{1}{3}$ **E** $\frac{2}{3}$

3.   The graph below shows the population of the city of Balonia over time.

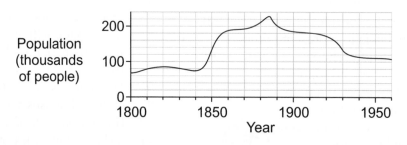

Use the graph to find the approximate population of Balonia in 1910.
Circle the correct option.

    A   80 000 people

    B   90 000 people

    C   160 000 people

    D   180 000 people

    E   190 000 people

Mrs Biggs asked each pupil in her class how many siblings they have.
She put the results in a bar chart.

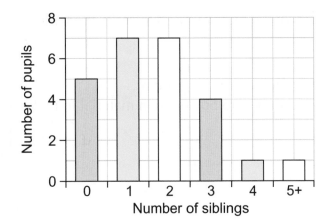

4. What percentage of the class have at least 5 siblings?

 %

5. Circle the statement below which could be false.
    A There are 25 pupils in Mrs Biggs' class.
    B One pupil has five siblings.
    C Six pupils have at least three siblings.
    D One in five pupils don't have any siblings.
    E Twelve pupils have fewer than two siblings.

A recipe says, 'Cook a chicken for 25 minutes, plus 5 minutes for every 100 g it weighs.'

6. Audrey has a chicken that weighs 1.1 kg. How long should she cook it for?
    Circle the correct option.

    A 50 minutes   **D** 1 hour 10 minutes
    B 1 hour 20 minutes   **E** 1 hour 50 minutes
    C 2 hours 25 minutes

7. Edward works out that he needs to cook his chicken for 2 hours and 5 minutes.
    How many grams does his chicken weigh?

 g

Tim makes a table. Each of the 4 legs has the dimensions 4 cm × 4 cm × 50 cm. The top is 20 cm × 20 cm × 1 cm.

8. What is the volume of the material used to make the table?

 cm³

9. The material that Tim uses costs 5p per cm³.
    How much does it cost him to buy enough material to make the table?

£

10. Mark has two identical triangles. Each triangle has sides with lengths of 5 cm, 9 cm and 13 cm. He joins the shortest sides together to form a parallelogram. What is the perimeter of the parallelogram?

 cm

Ethan has an extra-long strawberry lace. He cuts it in half and gives one half to his big sister. He cuts the other half into three equal pieces and gives two of them to his little brother to eat. He keeps the rest.

11. What fraction of the strawberry lace does Ethan keep? Circle the correct option.

    A ¹/₂
    B ²/₆
    C ¹/₃
    D ¹/₆
    E ²/₃

12. Each extra-long strawberry lace is made from 12 real strawberries.
    How many strawberries does Ethan's little brother eat?

/ 12

You have **10 minutes** to do this test. Work as quickly and accurately as you can.

1. What percentage of the grid below has been shaded?

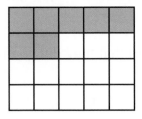

 %

2. Barry, Mick and Alex were born in the same year.
   Barry was born on 25th September, Mick was born on 12th June,
   and Alex was born on 1st August.

   How many days older than the youngest person is the oldest person?

   ⬜⬜⬜ days

Xan buys 5 bags of sweets. The numbers of sweets in each bag are listed here.

8, 6, 8, 8, 11

3. Which of the following statements is true? Circle the correct option.
   - **A** The total number of sweets is a square number.
   - **B** The total number of sweets is a multiple of 40.
   - **C** The total number of sweets is a prime number.
   - **D** The total number of sweets is a factor of 100.
   - **E** None of the above.

4. Xan buys another bag of sweets, which takes the overall mean number
   of sweets to 9. How many sweets are in this new bag?

   ⬜⬜

A group of people were asked whether they went on holiday last year.
The results are shown in a pie chart.

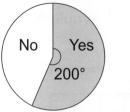

not drawn accurately

5. What fraction of the group said that they did go on holiday last year?
    Circle the correct option.

    A $^7/_{10}$ **B** $^4/_7$ **C** $^5/_6$ **D** $^2/_3$ **E** $^5/_9$

6. Sixteen people said that they did not go on holiday last year.
    How many people said that they did?

The total area of all the faces of a cube is 54 cm².

7. What is the cube's side length?

     cm

8. What is the cube's volume?

     cm³

9. On a coordinate grid, a counter is placed at the point with coordinates (–4, 5).
    The counter is moved two squares to the right, then diagonally across one square.
    Which of these points is the counter definitely not at? Circle the correct option.

    A (–1, 6)   **B** (–3, 4)   **C** (–3, 6)   **D** (–2, 6)   **E** (–1, 4)

10. One of the angles of a parallelogram is 111°.
What is the size of another of the angles that isn't 111°?

11. Four identical regular octagons are placed together to make the shape below.

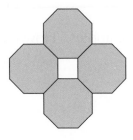

The square formed in the middle has a perimeter of 20 cm.
What is the outer perimeter of the shape? Circle the correct option.

A   84 cm   **B**   95 cm   **C**   100 cm   **D**   116 cm   **E**   125 cm

12. A type of plant pot can stack neatly, as shown below.

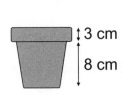 

‡3 cm

8 cm

What is the height, in cm, of a stack of x pots? Circle the correct option.

A $11x$

B $3x + 8$

C $8x + 3$

D $8 + 3 + x$

E $5x$

/ 12

You have **10 minutes** to do this test. Work as quickly and accurately as you can.

1.

> **Fruit Shop**
> Apple   15p
> Pineapple   95p

Joan buys a pineapple and three apples. How much does she spend?

£ .

2. Circle the shape below which has the greatest number of lines of symmetry.

A   **B**   **C**   **D**   **E**

3. Which of these is equal to three thousand and twenty-five millilitres?
    Circle the correct answer.

A 3.025 litres	**C** 3025 litres	**E** 0.3025 litres
B 3.25 litres	**D** 0.325 litres	

4. A cuboid has a length of 14 m, a width of 2 m and a volume of 280 m³.
    What is the cuboid's height?

 m

5. A crystal glass costs £17.50. A set of 4 glasses costs £56.
    What is the saving you would make by buying a set, instead of
    4 individual glasses? Write your answer as a percentage.

 %

The diagram below shows a pumpkin, a jar of peanut butter and a jar of mustard.

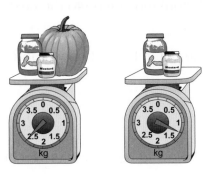

6. What is the mass of the pumpkin?

    ⬚.⬚⬚ kg

7. Brett buys the pumpkin, three jars of peanut butter and three jars of mustard.
    What is the total mass of his purchases?

    ⬚⬚.⬚⬚ kg

The chart below shows the total number of goals scored by all the teams in the first five rounds of an ice hockey tournament. The vertical axis has been left blank.

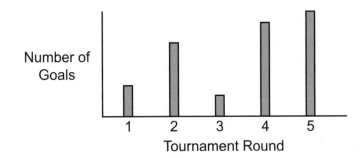

8. Which round had the third highest number of goals? Circle the correct answer.

    A 1   **B** 2   **C** 3   **D** 4   **E** 5

9. Which of these sets of data could be the numbers of goals scored
    in these five rounds? Circle the correct answer.

    A 28, 71, 21, 84, 96   **D** 90, 51, 10, 66, 89
    B 24, 68, 40, 90, 99   **E** 12, 24, 10, 35, 30
    C 30, 11, 19, 77, 88

10. Pam is sorting pencils into pencil pots. Each pot can hold 9 pencils.
    She fills each pencil pot before moving on to the next one.
    She has 570 pencils in total.

    How many pencils will she put in the last pencil pot?

11. Ken has drawn the graph below to help him convert between miles and kilometres.

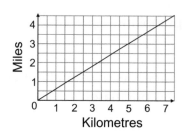

    He completes a 25 km run for charity.
    Use the graph to estimate how many miles Ken has run. Circle the correct answer.

    A   25 miles
    B   50 miles
    C   20 miles
    D   15 miles
    E   5 miles

12. Circle the expression below which is not equivalent to the others.

    A $12x \div 2$
    B $4x + 2$
    C $6x$
    D $3x \times 2$
    E $7x - x$

    / 12

You have **10 minutes** to do this test. Work as quickly and accurately as you can.

1. Two angles add up to make a right angle. One of them is 83°.
    What is the other angle?

     °

2. Nikki thinks of a number and divides it by 3. The remainder is 2.
    Which of these could have been her original number? Circle the correct answer.

    A   31
    B   60
    C   25
    D   23
    E   16

A sheet of card has a thickness of 0.5 mm.
Diego piles these sheets to a height of 8 cm.

3. How many sheets of card are in his pile?

4. Each sheet of card has a mass of 5 grams.
    Diego puts his pile of cards into a box of mass 250 g.
    What is the total mass of the box now it contains the pile of cards?
    Circle the correct answer.

    A   1250 g
    B   950 g
    C   1000 g
    D   1050 g
    E   850 g

The diagram below shows the point *A* with coordinates (–5, 4).

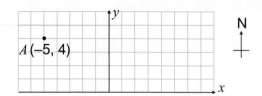

5. Point *A* is translated 8 squares east and 4 squares south, to give point *B*.
    What are the coordinates of *B*?

6. Point *B* is reflected in the *y*-axis, to give point *C*.
    What are the coordinates of *C*? Circle the correct answer.

    A (0, –3)   **B** (0, 3)   **C** (–3, 0)   **D** (3, –3)   **E** (–3, 3)

7. Althea is thinking of a number. She says, 'the number is a factor of 60,
    a multiple of 5, and 1 less than a square number'.
    Which of these is the number she is thinking of? Circle the correct answer.

    A   10
    B   3
    C   35
    D   48
    E   15

A recipe uses 100 g of flour, 100 g of sugar and 80 g of butter.

8. Damian has 120 g of butter, and wants to use it all in this recipe.
    What total weight of flour and sugar should he use, in grams?

     g

9. Damian realises he only has 60 g of sugar, so can't use all of his butter.
    How many grams of butter will he have left over when he's
    finished making the recipe?

    g

10. Circle the statement below which is incorrect.

   A   2% is equivalent to 0.02
   B   0.25 is equivalent to $^1/_4$
   C $^4/_{10}$ is equivalent to 40%
   D $^3/_5$ is equivalent to 0.6
   E   35% is equivalent to 3.5

11. The first six terms in a sequence are 1, 4, 9, 16, 25 and 36.
    What is the eleventh term in the sequence?

12. Sheryl cuts a triangle from a rectangular piece of card, as shown.

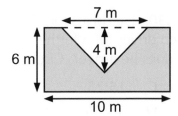

7 m

4 m

6 m

10 m

What is the area of the shape left over? Circle the correct answer.

   A   60 m²
   B   54 m²
   C   44 m²
   D   46 m²
   E   32 m²

/ 12

Test 29

You have **10 minutes** to do this test. Work as quickly and accurately as you can.

1. Liam asks the members of his art class to name their favourite material
    to work with. He displays the results in the pie chart shown.

There are 28 people in his art class.
How many people said that paint was their favourite?

2. Jamie sets off from home at 13:30. He drives for 25 minutes, stops at a service
    station for 10 minutes, and then drives for a further hour and a half before arriving
    at his destination. What time does he arrive? Circle the correct answer.

    A   14:05   **C**   15:25   **E**   14:50
    B   15:35   **D**   15:05

3. The shape shown below is made out of seven cubes.

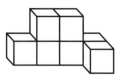

    Circle the option below which shows the view when
    looking down from directly above the shape.

    A   **B**   **C**   **D**   **E**

Aiden has 3 stripy ties, 5 spotty ties and 12 plain ties.

4. What fraction of his ties aren't spotty? Circle the correct answer.

   A $^3/_{20}$ **B** $^{17}/_{20}$ **C** $^3/_4$ **D** $^1/_4$ **E** $^3/_5$

5. What is the ratio of plain ties to stripy ties? Give your answer in its simplest form.

6. The shape shown is reflected in the dotted mirror line.

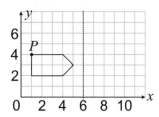

   What is the new position of vertex *P*? Circle the correct answer.

   A (1, 4)

   B (4, 1)

   C (11, 4)

   D (12, 4)

   E (10, 4)

Elise and Lara have a total of 120 trading cards between them.
Elise has three times as many as Lara.

7. How many does Elise have?

8. Rashid has twice as many cards as Elise. What percentage
   of all of Elise, Lara and Rashid's cards belong to Rashid?

9. Sebastian cycles a total of 120 miles over a period of 5 days.
   What is the mean distance he cycles each day?

    miles

10. The shape below is made by cutting a rectangle from a larger rectangle.

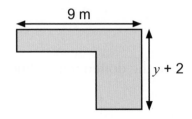

9 m

$y + 2$

   Circle the expression below which gives the shape's perimeter.

   A $22 + 4y$

   B $11 + 2y$

   C $22 + 2y$

   D $20 + y$

   E $11 + y$

11. The formula for finding the nth term in a sequence is $10 - 4n$.
    What is the third term in the sequence? Circle the correct answer.

   A   7

   B   −33

   C   3

   D   −2

   E   −4

12. Which number term in the sequence has value 2?

   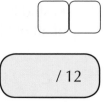

   / 12

10

You have **10 minutes** to do this test. Work as quickly and accurately as you can.

1. Yasmine sells 120324 copies of her new novel in its first week.
    What is this figure in words? Circle the correct answer.

    A   one hundred and twenty three thousand and twenty four

    B   twelve thousand, three hundred and twenty four

    C   one hundred and twenty thousand, three hundred and twenty four

    D   one million, two hundred thousand, three hundred and twenty four

    E   one hundred and twenty million, three hundred and twenty four thousand

2. Marissa is painting the front of a wooden gate. The front of the gate is a rectangle
    with sides of length 3 m and 4 m. She buys a tin of paint which will cover an
    area of 48 m². What fraction of the tin of paint is left over when she has finished?
    Circle the correct answer.

    A ¹/₅   **B** ¹/₄   **C** ³/₅   **D** ³/₄   **E** ¹/₂

3. George is reading a book which has 860 pages.
    He reads at an average rate of two pages per minute.
    Since starting the book, he has read for 1 hour and 20 minutes.

    How many pages does he still have left to read?

4. A square has a perimeter of 48 m. What is its area? Circle the correct answer.

    A 48 m²   **D** 132 m²

    B 12 m²   **E** 96 m²

    C 144 m²

Madison's bookshelf contains 200 books. 22% of her books are horror stories, 37% are sci-fi stories, and the rest are non-fiction.

5. How many of her books are non-fiction?

6. 34 of all her books are hardback.
   What percentage of her books is this?

 %

7. The diagram below shows an isosceles triangle.

What is the size of angle *a*?

 °

8. The pictogram below shows the amount of time Henry spent playing different sports during one week.

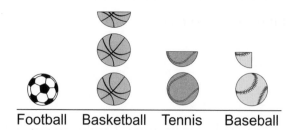

| Football | Basketball | Tennis | Baseball |

Key:
1 ball = 60 minutes

How many more minutes did Henry spend playing basketball than baseball during this week?

minutes

9. The table below shows the number of pairs of different kinds of footwear in Reuben's wardrobe.

Type	Number of pairs
Smart shoes	2
Boots	5
Trainers	8
Slippers	1

What fraction of his footwear collection is either boots or slippers?
Circle the correct answer.

A $\frac{1}{16}$

B $\frac{1}{4}$

C $\frac{1}{2}$

D $\frac{3}{8}$

E $\frac{5}{16}$

Malcolm thinks of five numbers. He writes four of them down:

13, 7, 9, 16

He says, 'the mean of the five numbers is 12'.

10. What is the fifth number Malcolm was thinking of?

11. Malcolm thinks of a sixth number. The mean is now 10.
What is the sixth number?

12. $\boxed{x^2 > 2 \times 25 - 1}$

x is a positive whole number.
What is the smallest number that x could be?

/ 12

 Test 31

Time for a break! These puzzles are a great way to practise your maths skills.

Equal Shapes

Split each shape on the right in half to make two identical smaller shapes.

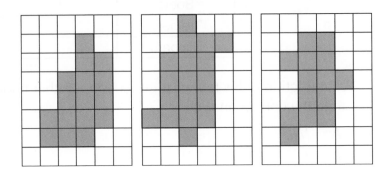

Elevenses

Amelia writes down a trick to find out if a number will divide exactly by 11. She uses the trick to show that 3091 divides exactly by 11:

1. Add together all the digits in the even positions:

   3091   0 + 1 = 1

2. Add together all the digits in the odd positions:

   3091   3 + 9 = 12

3. Subtract the smaller sum from the larger sum:

   12 − 1 = 11

4. If the result is 0 or a multiple of 11, then the number divides exactly by 11. ✓

Use Amelia's trick to answer the following:

- Does 29 524 divide exactly by 11?

- Does 312 581 divide exactly by 11?

- What is the only number between 2 165 860 and 2 165 869 that divides exactly by 11?

M6XPDE1